YOU'RE ABOUT TO MAKE AN EXCITING NEW ACQUAINTANCE...

I KNOW, I KNOW ... OTHER CATS SIT
IN FRONT OF MOUSEHOLES
ALL DAY TOO ...

STILL ...
I'M A LITTLE WORRIED.

WHOSE CAT SWALLOWED THE SOAP?

I'M NOT BEING RUDE, I JUST DON'T WANT HER TO GET STUCK.

JUST LIKE KIDS - THEY HATE TO TAKE MEDICINE
UNTIL YOU PUT IT ON A SUGAR CUBE...

GO HOME GUYS . . . SHE'S GOT A HEADACHE

WE'D GET A LOT MORE
PEACE IF HE HAD HIS OWN TV.

MARTHA, GET HER
OUT OF HERE
WHILE WE PRACTICE !

SINCE SHE STARTED WATCHING COMMERCIALS,
SHE INSISTS ON PICKING HER OWN FOOD. . .

SHE'S NOT OURS. . .
SHE WAS ALREADY HERE WHEN WE MOVED IN.

OH, THAT ONE... IT ALMOST GOT AWAY.

MOTHER, LOOK, AN ANGEL!